بسم الله الرحمن الرحيم

و صلى الله على سيدنا و نبينا محمد و على آله الطيبين الطاهرين

In the Name of Allah, the Beneficent, the Merciful

May Allah Bless our Master and Prophet,
Muhammad and his Good and Purified Progeny

The Champion of Islam
A Collection of Eight Stories about Imam Ali (a.s)

Editor-in-Chief: Ahmed Haneef
Translated by Mirza Mohammed Abbas Raza
and Adapted by Ahmed Haneef
from the original book <u>The Young Warrior</u> *by Muslim Naasiri*
Editors: Rasheeda Haneef, Hajar Khadijah Z. and Hamid Reza
Graphic Designers: Ahmad Jafari and Mahdi Muharrer
Publisher: Islamic International Foundation of Cooperation
21ˢᵗ Feb Books
With special thanks to Seyyed Amir Husaini
2ⁿᵈ Edition July 2004
ISBN 964-06-5159-1

Contents

A Brief Outline of the Life of Imam Ali (a.s)

Name: Ali (a.s)

Title: Amir al Mu'minin, Murtaza

Nickname: Abul Hasan

Father: Abu Talib

Mother: Fatima-bintul-Assad

Birth Date: Thirteenth of Rajab, (c.600 C.E.) thirty years after the Event of the *fil* (the Elephant)

Place of Birth: the Ka'ba (the House of Allah), in the city of Mecca

Duration of Imamat: Thirty years

Duration of Khalifate: Four years and nine months

Date of Martyrdom: Twenty first of Ramadan, the fortieth year after the Hijrah

Place of Burial: Najaf al Ashraf

Collection of his Speeches and Sermons: Nahjul-Balaghah

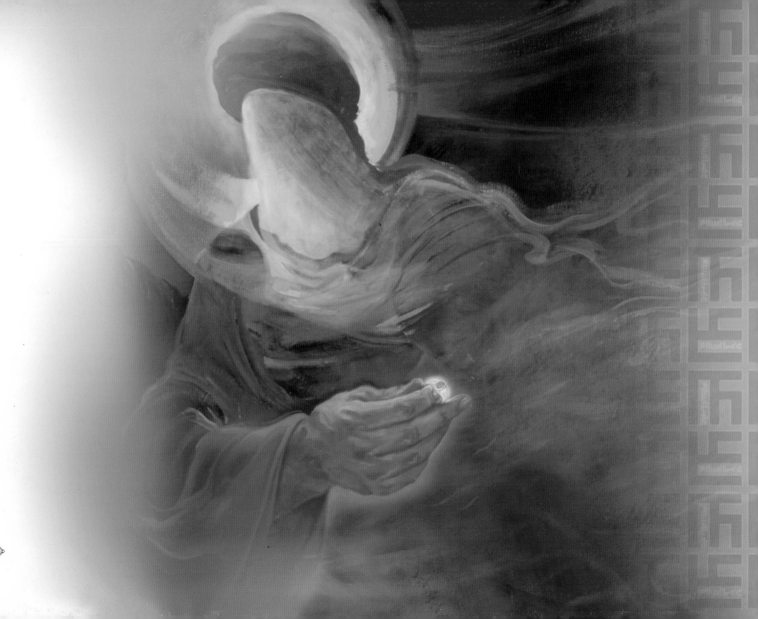

Ali lived with his father Abu Talib in Mecca until he was ten years old. A drought then occurred, whereby the Prophet (s) agreed to take him under his care. Ali was with the Prophet for twenty-three years and was a great help to him in several difficulties and wars.

After the demise of the Prophet of Islam, conspirators oppressed him usurping his right to the leadership of the Muslims and he remained isolated in his house. To preserve the newly established Islam, Ali kept silent for twenty-five years in the face of the injustices inflicted upon him. After the murder of Uthman, the people were thirsty for Ali's justice and were tired of oppression by government officials. Therefore, they rushed to Ali to pledge the oath of allegiance to him.

Hazrat Ali ruled over the Muslim *Ummah* for four years and nine months. During this period he was constantly fighting wars to maintain his authority and apply his perfect justice. The most important wars were Siffin, Jamal and Nahrawan. In the early hours of the morning of the nineteenth of Ramadan, in the fortieth year of the Hijrah, he was struck by the sword of the most vicious of men while absorbed in *salaat* (prayer). He drank from the cup of martyrdom two days later, on the twenty-first of Ramadan.

Imam Ali is not only known as a great champion but is also known for his profundity, intelligence, and sagacity. Sayyid Radi, one of the most prominent scholars of the Shiite school of thought has collected the Imam's *khutbah* (sermons) and sayings in a book entitled the *Nahjul Balaghah* from which one can learn a perfect and proper way of life.

The Light in the House of Allah

A large crowd of the men and women of Mecca had gathered around the Ka'ba in the city in order to see with their own eyes what was going to happen. Some of them had pushed through the crowd in order to get near the wall of the Ka'ba. When they saw the thin crack in the wall that indicated where it had opened, they were struck with astonishment. After feeling and touching the crack they went and told people all over the city,

"By Allah, the stones of the wall split and Fatima-bintul-Assad went in and remained inside for three days. If we did not see this wonderful sight with our own eyes we would not have believed it ourselves!"

Everyone was waiting to see what would happen to the wife of Abu Talib. Three days had gone by since she had entered the Ka'ba and since then there had been no news about her. The people had tried everything possible to enter however, the door remained locked. The huge fissure in the wall had closed with only a thin line remaining.

The news spread quickly through the city and nearby towns. Curious, groups from different tribes and towns in the vicinity of Mecca excitedly made their way towards the Ka'ba in order to witness this strange incident. Was the wife of Abu Talib going to come out? Only the occasional cries of a baby punctuated the anxious silence. Their wait seemed fruitless. The third day had almost come to an end and the sun, spreading its light over the wall of the Ka'ba seemed more desperate than anyone else to see the new born child and its mother. Abu Talib, sitting in a corner with his head on his knee was consumed with concern for his wife and child while Muhammad stood next to him to give him support. The cries of the baby got louder and everyone rushed towards the crack prompting Hamza with his powerful voice to ask them to step back. Suddenly, the wall moved slightly and a few weather-beaten stones fell to the ground. The people who were in front moved back in fear and bewilderment.

One woman said, "Maybe the mother is dead."

An old lady answered her angrily, "Allah forbid! If she dies then who will take care of Abu Talib's son?"

Someone else shouted, "So why doesn't she say anything?"

"Look! The wall moved a bit again!" said a young man standing upon a tall idol, but no one paid any attention to him.

Everyone wanted to know the fate of Fatima-bintul-Assad. While Hamza held back the men, a few women went forward to find a way into the Ka'ba. Abu Talib rose to his feet, hoping to see his child while being fearful of losing his beloved wife. Muhammad continued standing beside him but this time, he was whispering something under his breath.

Abu Talib's heart was beating so loudly, it almost drowned out the murmur of the crowd. As he took a few steps towards the building, the wall of the Ka'ba cleaved open a bit more and a woman standing by cried out loud and fainted.

Abu Sufyan said, "By Laat and 'Uzza! If I had not seen the wall of the Ka'ba crack open with my own eyes, I would never have believed it."

Once again, Hamza forced the men to stand aside as more stones and cakes of dried mud fell down.

It was a scene to be treasured throughout the ages. The wall of the Ka'ba split open allowing the sun's rays to shine inside like a carpet.

In the torturous moments that followed, everyone was desperate to see what was going to happen. As the aperture in the wall grew larger, and the view inside the Ka'ba became clearer, the women who had advanced to the front of the crowd suddenly broke out in loud cries of astonishment. On hearing them, Abbas, Abu Talib's brother, leapt inside and stood motionless, allowing his eyes to get used to the soft darkness of the windowless room. His eyes were drawn to an ever-increasing radiance that seemed to grow in intensity. As his eyes adjusted themselves to the dark, he realized that this blissful light was emanating from Fatima herself, and she appeared as if she was clothed in sheets of light. On seeing her still alive and bathed in that radiant glow, the crowd broke out in whoops and cries of joy as they made way for her to emerge from the Holy House.

Fatima-bintul-Assad came out smiling, cuddling a baby wrapped snugly in a white cloth. She stood at the edge of the cleft for a moment, lifted her eyes to the heavens and whispered a prayer of thanks to Allah, then stepped away from the enormous crack which miraculously closed up again. On seeing his beloved wife, Abu Talib was beside himself with joy.

The women flanked Fatima on both sides and ushered her towards Abu Talib. Hamza, who was standing by in a corner supporting himself on his bow came towards them with tears of joy, beaming with pride. This occasion reflected that a great honor had been destined for the family of Abdul Muttalib. Fatima came up to Abu Talib with a smile and placed the babe into his hands saying, "It's a boy", the father kissed the child and wondered what name he should call him.

The boy was very beautiful and a charming smile often flitted across his angelic face, but he never opened his eyes. Everyone wondered why the baby did not want to open his eyes but they soon got their answer. In the very moment he was put in the arms of his cousin Muhammad he looked up and gazed at the face of his older cousin, cooing with happiness. They looked at each other as if they had known each other before and miraculously exchanged whispered words.

Fatima-bintul-Assad is narrated to have said that while she was standing near the crack in the wall, she had heard a mysterious voice from the heavens that said that the boy should be called Ali since his birth took place in a miraculous way.

Henceforth the newborn boy was known as Ali, meaning the Most High, because Allah gave him this high honor by inviting him to His house for his birth and gave him His name.

The First to Pray with the Prophet

A cool breeze ruffled the branches of the trees and brushed the leaves of the date palm that grew in the middle of the yard. Ali stood at the edge of a well engrossed in watching the rays of the sun as they played between the leaves and branches of the date palm. The light shone in patches of varying sizes as it broke through the foliage. The birds chirped happily while flitting to and fro between the branches and the roofs of the houses. Ali sensed that there was something special about that day. He had been up before dawn and since then he had not gone back to sleep. He drew a bucket full of water from the well and washed his hands and face. The cool water was pure and clean. When the water inside the well ceased moving, he could see his reflection as clearly as in a mirror. The courtyard was peaceful and calm. Ali paced around the yard wondering what important events the day would hold. He walked past his cousin's room and saw Muhammad as usual prostrating, bowing and raising his hands towards the heavens while softly whispering his prayers. Ali walked towards the portico and sat listening to his cousin's soothing voice coming from the room. While he was absorbed in thought he heard Muhammad saying,

"Ali! Could you come here please?"

He ran towards the room, and saw his cousin, Muhammad standing near the window. The morning sun had already illuminated half of the room reaching as far as Muhammad's straw mat. The room had

مسجد النبی

the scent of sweet perfume. He gave salaams to his cousin from the doorway. Muhammad returned the salaams with a pleasant smile and invited him in, treating him as if he was much older than his ten years. Ali came in and Muhammad placed his hand upon his shoulder. He looked at Muhammad and broke out in a broad smile because he always loved to see his cousin and he knew that he must have had important news for him to call him so early in the morning.

"Ali!" Muhammad said, "I have been chosen by Allah as a Messenger and I must invite mankind towards the worship of the one and only Allah. I would like to ask you to accept this religion."

The way Muhammad spoke to him filled Ali's heart with joy, for he knew that this religion was the best of all faiths for the best of all men was chosen for this mission. He was a man who worshipped Allah day and night. A man who was known as *al-Amin* (the Trustworthy) and everyone believed him to be truthful. All of them sought advice from him whenever they were faced with problems and difficulties. Without hesitation, Ali immediately announced his support and affiliation with the new religion saying,

"I bear witness that there is no God but Allah and Muhammad is the Messenger of Allah". With tears in his eyes, the Prophet embraced him and said, "I'm proud of you O Ali."

For this reason, Ali was known as the first man to accept Islam and the first person to pray along with Prophet Muhammad.

Forty Daggers Against One Man

"He is over there, alone, sleeping."

"So why don't we attack?"

"Calm down, when the entire neighborhood has gone to sleep, we'll cut him to pieces."

"I think he is gone, he's escaped!"

"You fool, can't you see him? He's tossing and turning under his blanket."

"Prepare the daggers to taste Muhammad's blood!"

The night was cold and chilly, and when the wind blew it merged with the muttered words of the idol worshippers. Lying in bed, Ali was looking at the moon through the window and wondering where the Prophet could be at that moment. Was he still in Mecca? Or had he crossed its borders by now?

The sharp daggers glinted in the moonlight, impatient for the pure body of the Prophet as the conspirators surrounded the house on all sides. The lamps of the houses of Mecca were now being extinguished one after another and silence fell over the city like a soft blanket. Abu Jahl placed his hand over his sharp dagger and moving towards a crack in the wall, said, "Muhammad thinks that if we do not believe in him, we will be put in the fires of Hell". He asked the man watching the door, "Is he awake or asleep?"

"He moved a bit, but yes, he's sleeping."

The night was passing peacefully. Ali turned in the bed and pulled the green Yemeni cloth over his face thinking about the Prophet's words that evening.

The Archangel Gabriel had told the Prophet that the polytheists had planned to kill him. This news worried Ali, so he was relieved when the Prophet had asked him to sleep in his bed in order to make his escape.

"If I sleep in your bed O Prophet, will you be saved?"

The Prophet smiled and answered in the affirmative. He left Ali in the room who then went to the bed and covered himself with the Prophet's blanket, hiding his face. He was breathing calmly listening to the whispers of the idol worshippers as they surrounded the house. It was possible that at any moment tens of daggers would cut him to pieces, but he smiled saying to himself that if the life of the Prophet would be saved, then death would be like a cup of sweet nectar to him.

He lay there watching the stars through the window and thought about his noble cousin. The thoughts of the Prophet's smile, words and compassion flooded his mind and he fell asleep. As he mentioned later, this was the best sleep he had ever had.

The assassins jumped over the wall and stealthily went to the room. Abu Jahl, the leader, said,

"He is sound asleep, we should not waste time, let's attack all at once."

Silently, they entered the room, holding their daggers ready, their faces covered to hide their identities and stealthily moved towards the bed.

The horses outside started neighing, a rooster called out a warning and the moon hid itself behind the clouds. There was tension in the air.

"It would be better if we removed the cover from over his face."

"He'll wake-up!"

"What difference would it make? He's going to be sliced up anyway."

Abu Jahl came up to the figure sleeping in the bed with his head and face covered. Nervously chewing on his mask, Abu Jahl slipped the cover off the face while they all stood ready with daggers drawn. At that very moment, the moon came out from behind the clouds and moonlight flooded the room making the face of the sleeping figure easily discernible. It was not Muhammad, but Ali who was now wide awake and looking back at them with more amusement than consternation. The would-be assassins were shocked; Abu Jahl's jaw dropped in surprise and the dagger fell from his hands onto his feet.

"By our gods, Laat and 'Uzza, Muhammad is a sorcerer!", they said.

With a mixture of anger and astonishment in his voice, Abu Jahl asked Ali, "Where is your cousin?"

Ali looked at the shining disc of the moon through the window and smiled. He said, "Did you place him in my care so that you are entitled to ask me about his whereabouts?"

"But do you know where he is?"

Ali replied, "You wanted him to leave Mecca."

Abu Jahl stormed out of the room shouting in anger; the veins of his forehead and neck stuck out like black-red snakes, "Muhammad's gone! We must find him! We can not allow him to escape our grasp!"

The Young Warrior

"Is there someone who can fight me? Why are you all so silent? Am I here to fight the dead? Come onto the battlefield, don't you know that my sword is thirsty for your blood?"

The Muslim soldiers stayed completely silent, unresponsive to the challenges.

"I've heard that you believe when you die in battle you'll go to Heaven. Well I'm ready to send you there!"

They were waiting for word from their commander. They had fought many battles but never before had they faced such a formidable foe. The fighter sat on his horse and galloped from one end of the front line to the other, his enormous body looked like a mountain built of iron. He was carrying a heavy bow upon his strong shoulders and was skillfully wielding his sword in the air.

The warriors in the opposing ranks looked sheepishly at the rider, they had heard of his victories, no man was able to stand up to him and survive. As he galloped to and fro in front of them, the troops recoiled in fear. However, despite the reputation and the awesomeness of the presence of this hitherto invincible fighter, there was a youth on the other side who seemed quite unmoved and unperturbed by all that was going on. He remained calm and tranquil. His feet were firmly planted on the ground and he stood like a pillar holding his sword with full determination.

Suddenly, the champion of the unbelievers came close to the opposing army as he skillfully pulled on the reins of his black horse. It started moving in a circle showing its sparkling white teeth. The great warrior shouted,

"Are you all deaf or made of stones? Where are your fighters? I'm getting hoarse from yelling so much. You're nothing but a bunch of cowards!"

The silence from the Muslim side was deafening. The commander, a strong man with a shining tranquil face, his sword hanging loosely from his back, stood in front of his soldiers, and said,

"Somebody get up and silence the evil of this man!" But no one moved. They were petrified with fear. The Prophet walked towards them with firm decisive steps to evaluate the psychological effects the boasting of the enemy champion had upon the morale of his troops. Some of the men were trembling in fear and some had turned pale but when he came upon the young Ali, he saw courage in his manly face and an urge to silence the bragging of this warrior.

The challenge of the enemy warrior had disturbed his opponents and was leading to chaos in the ranks. The men had started to murmur,

"We should sign a truce; if not we'll all be killed!"

"That man can defeat a thousand men!"

"We had better make peace with them!"

As the soldiers murmured, only the young warrior seemed to be ready to answer the Prophet's call. He rose to his feet for a second time to answer the boastful challenge of the powerful pagan. The commander looked at him with encouragement but made him sit for a second time. All of the soldiers looked at the young fighter with anxiety and hope. They were reminded of his previous victories and how courageously he had engaged the enemy on the battlefield and had emerged victorious. This time,

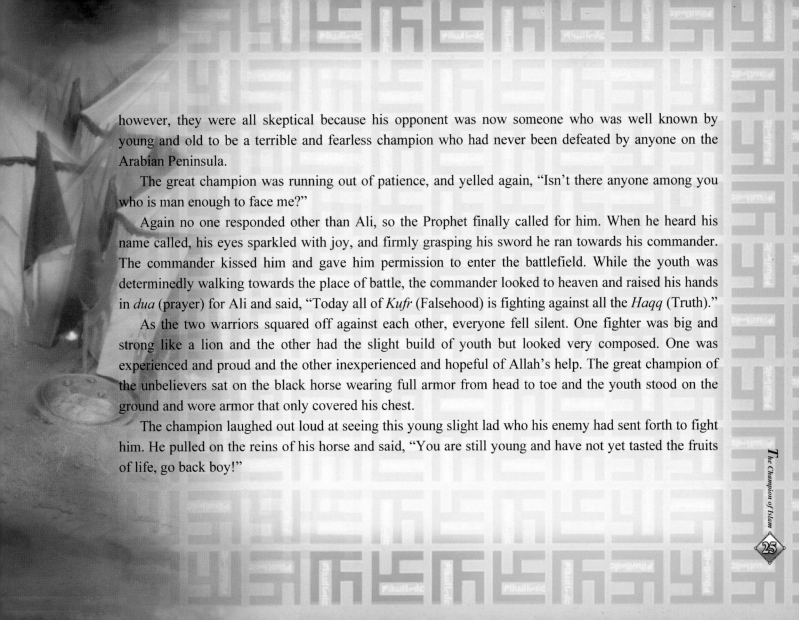

however, they were all skeptical because his opponent was now someone who was well known by young and old to be a terrible and fearless champion who had never been defeated by anyone on the Arabian Peninsula.

The great champion was running out of patience, and yelled again, "Isn't there anyone among you who is man enough to face me?"

Again no one responded other than Ali, so the Prophet finally called for him. When he heard his name called, his eyes sparkled with joy, and firmly grasping his sword he ran towards his commander. The commander kissed him and gave him permission to enter the battlefield. While the youth was determinedly walking towards the place of battle, the commander looked to heaven and raised his hands in *dua* (prayer) for Ali and said, "Today all of *Kufr* (Falsehood) is fighting against all the *Haqq* (Truth)."

As the two warriors squared off against each other, everyone fell silent. One fighter was big and strong like a lion and the other had the slight build of youth but looked very composed. One was experienced and proud and the other inexperienced and hopeful of Allah's help. The great champion of the unbelievers sat on the black horse wearing full armor from head to toe and the youth stood on the ground and wore armor that only covered his chest.

The champion laughed out loud at seeing this young slight lad who his enemy had sent forth to fight him. He pulled on the reins of his horse and said, "You are still young and have not yet tasted the fruits of life, go back boy!"

The young warrior responded,

"I invite you to accept the reality of *la ilaaha illa 'Llah Muhammad ar Rasul Allah* (there is no god but Allah and Muhammad is the Messenger of Allah)"

The giant got angry and said, "Do not ask this of me!"

The youth replied, "If you accept this, it would be good for you, but I also have another offer for you."

The great warrior said, "What other offer?"

The young warrior said, "Return the way you came!"

The champion of champions laughed out loud and said, "Never! If I return, don't you think the women will laugh at me? O little one, I tell you again to leave here because killing you is not going to increase my status."

The youth replied, "If you do not want to accept Islam and return which is better for you then get down from your horse and fight me."

The great fighter got down from his black horse and said, "I don't think that there is anyone who would find fault with me for killing you, but I would hate doing that because you are still so young."

The young warrior answered, "But I would like to kill you!"

The young warrior's reply infuriated the giant's heart and he was overcome with rage.

He yelled, "You little punk!"

The young warrior grasped his sword and quickly drew it from the scabbard, the face of the fighter turned purple with fury and his eyes saw blood. The young fighter, holding his sword ran towards the giant who also let out a loud war cry and rushed towards him. When they clashed a cloud of dust surrounded the two combatants, the sounds of clashing steel and of swords smashing into shields could be heard. The soldiers on both sides saw the massive sword of the champion swinging like a deadly thunderbolt amidst the dust. Suddenly the sword of the powerful champion was coming straight for the head of the young man. Ali quickly raised his shield to block the blow, but the force was too strong to withstand. The sword split his shield and continued downward striking the head of the young warrior, his helmet went flying and blood ran down his face as the enemy's sword found its mark. On seeing this, the enemy camp let out a shout of joy. It seemed that victory was imminent but their expectation was premature. The fight was far from over. Fortunately, the shield neutralized the blow of the sword somewhat, and the wound was only superficial. As the enemy champion was falling upon him from above, Ali, crouching under his upraised shield, swung at the leg of the invincible champion and severed it below the knee. With a dreadful scream that punctuated the expectant silence of the onlookers, the giant foe immediately collapsed to the ground and the young warrior gave the victory cry, *"Allahu Akbar!"*

When the dust settled, the men saw the figure of the youth standing with sword in hand over the great former champion who was writhing in agony on the ground. The young man readied himself to deliver the final blow. Ever defiant and full of hate, the defeated giant spat upon Ali. This clearly angered the young warrior. He wiped the bloody saliva off his face, put his sword down and walked a few steps away from his enemy. The defeated fighter looked at the victorious youth with surprise, he thought to himself, "If I was in his place I would have cut me to pieces for that insult."

Ali collected himself and after a few moments, he walked purposefully towards the fallen fighter and dispatched him with one swift blow. Then Ali returned to his commander.

On the enemy side, the army commanders were in shock when they finally realized that their undefeatable champion, the hero of the polytheists was really dead. They were overcome by self-doubt and fear. The sister of their dead hero, on the other hand, was seen crying and smiling intermittently. She placed her hands over the untouched jewelry of her brother and was amazed that her brother's killer did not loot a single piece! She thought to herself that the victor was truly a courageous and upright man who had not killed her brother for any worldly purpose. She looked up, wiping the tears from her eyes and asked, "Who is the great man who killed my brother?"

Someone replied, "Ali the son of Abu Talib."

The lady smiled and took her brother's body in her arms and said, "I am proud that my brother has been killed by the sword of such a great, courageous hero."

Later on Ali was asked why he changed his mind when he was about to kill Amr ibn Abdu Wudd the first time in the Battle of the Trench.

He replied, "When he spit on my face, I got angry, so I waited for my anger to subside and then I killed him only for the sake of Allah."

Pomegranates from Heaven

Ali was anxiously going from one shop to the other. Huddled against the cold wind that brought news of the approaching winter, he had gone to practically every shop but unfortunately could not find a single pomegranate. He was desperately trying to keep the promise he had made to his wife that he would find her one.

The pomegranate season was over and they were no longer available in the shops. Ali did not like going back home empty handed because this was Fatima's only wish and he desperately wanted to fulfill it.

Tired from his efforts, he stood under the shade of a wall for a while and looked towards the sky. It was almost noon. He whispered a prayer and started to walk towards the only store he had not visited. The old storekeeper, his hands shaking from old age, was weighing out a few dates for a slave girl. Ali waited until he was finished with his customer and then asked him if he knew anyone who sold pomegranates. The old storekeeper cleaning his hands with a cloth smiled at the young man and said, "Have you been looking for pomegranates since this morning? When I saw you passing by my store I said to myself, that this man looks worried."

Ali told him that if he could only get just one that would be fine and he would surely pay a good price for it. The old man raised his gray eyebrows, stepped outside the store and gathered up the palm-mat of dates he had spread out in the sun and said,

"If you pay good money then you might probably be able to get it from Simon because I saw him a week ago bringing a box full of pomegranates from Ta'if, but you must hurry if you want it."

On hearing this Ali was filled with joy and after thanking the old man, he hurried towards Simon's shop. He wished he had asked the old Jew earlier in order not to delay his wife's wish. The dusty earth was moving fast under Ali's feet as he tried his best to reach the Bani Qurayza neighborhood quickly. Finally he arrived at Simon's house and stood for a moment at the doorstep. The wooden door was big, beautiful, and decorated with iron roses. He knocked but there was no answer. He stepped back and looked at the high walls of the house and knocked on the door again. Just then he heard the footsteps of someone coming.

A sleepy, puffy faced Simon opened the door. He was surprised to see the Prophet's son-in-law and asked him what it was that had brought him to his house.

Ali greeted Simon and said, "I heard that you had brought some pomegranates from your tribe to sell." Simon scratched his stomach and said, "So?"

"I have a sick person to look after, so if you have any remaining I would really appreciate it."

Simon shook his head and said, "I sold them already."

Ali said desperately, "Could you please look inside your house? Perhaps there might be one pomegranate left."

Simon laughed and said, "Are you saying that I don't know what's in my house? I am positive that there is not a single one left."

Ali was just about to go back home when Simon's wife said, "Wait, I have one."

Simon let Ali in and his wife went to get it. She soon came back with a big red pomegranate and Simon took it from her, threw it in the air a couple of times and then passed it to Ali. The pomegranate felt as if it was breathing in his hands, and he could feel the grains through its thin skin. He placed four dirhams in Simon's hand and Simon said, "But this pomegranate is no more than half a Dirham."

Ali smiled and said with full confidence, "The rest is for your wife who had saved it." Simon stood looking at Ali while he slowly disappeared from view and thought to himself that if the fruit had been one hundred dirhams, Ali would still have bought it.

Happy to have finally found a pomegranate and thinking of presenting it to his wife, Ali quickly walked through the alleys towards his home. Taking a shortcut he decided to pass through a run down part of the city to avoid going through the pottery market which would have made his way longer. He was passing by the dilapidated and abandoned homes when suddenly he heard a cry for help. Ali stopped and looked around; it appeared to be a hungry old man searching for food. He went towards the direction of the sound and saw an old blind man with shaky hands trying to find his staff among the ruins. The man's clothes were dirty and dusty and from their color it was obvious that he was not from Medina. He did not have even the strength to stand up so Ali went up to him. The old man sniffed the air and said, "O what a sweet-smell, someone must have brought a box of pomegranates into these ruins." Ali sat next to him and asked him about how he was and from where he came.

The old man coughed and said, "I am from Madian and I have a lot of debts, I came here to ask for help and I got sick." Ali said, "And now what is your wish?" The old man coughed and said, "I smell pomegranates and if you could give me one, Allah will give you in return."

Ali looked at the stranger's wrinkled face and said, "There is only one pomegranate left in this whole city and I am taking it for my wife, who is ill." Then he paused a bit and continued, "However, I will never deprive a dear old man like you."

The blind old man laughed joyously and nodded his head and when he heard the cracking sound of the pomegranate being opened, he wet his lips in anticipation. Ali carefully divided the pomegranate into two and made sure that not even a grain dropped on the ground. He put one half on a stone and the other half he gradually fed the old man. Every time the old man took a bite from the pomegranate he would exclaim,

"O what a tasty pomegranate! May Allah make you fortunate, young man!"

After the old man had his share, Ali stood up and picked up the other half of the pomegranate and said, "Do you want anything else?" The old man said, "I can still smell the sweet scent of pomegranates, can you offer me the remaining one too? It will be a great favor to me and I will thank you for it."

Ali looked at the sky, the sun was directly overhead and all was quiet except for the coughing of this old man. If he fulfilled the old man's request, what would he take for the daughter of the Prophet? On one hand there was Fatima who was waiting for him to bring her the fruit and on the other was the old blind man's heart which he didn't want to break. He said a quiet prayer and took the stranger into the shade. There he made him sit and respectfully gave him the other half of the pomegranate.

When the old man finished eating it, he raised his thin shaky hands in prayer for Ali. On his way home Ali was concerned about what answer he would give Fatima when she asked for the pomegranate. He had promised her that morning to bring her one. Now what could he do? How could he enter the house without the long awaited pomegranate? Ali stood for a while in the yard and leaning against the wall implored Allah's help. The yard was quiet as he entered the house wishing his wife were asleep, so she would not see him coming home empty handed. As he was passing near her room he glanced inside and to his astonishment he saw that she was awake and was eating a pomegranate. He went into her room and could not believe his eyes. There were big red pomegranates in front of Fatima, one of them she had cut into two and she was busy enjoying one of the halves.

The daughter of the Prophet gave a sweet smile to her faithful husband and he saw the contentment in her eyes. He put his hand upon the wooden frame of the door and asked, "Who brought you these pomegranates?" Fatima smiled and from the smile he understood she was surprised at this question and this smile satisfied his heart.

"O my uncle's son, a few minutes ago there was a sudden knock at the door. Someone brought these pomegranates and said that you had sent them!"

The Unconquerable Fort

The cries of the wounded soldiers were carried away by the gusts of a cold wind as the sun set over the bloodied fields. Ali was sitting in the corner of a tent holding his head in pain. Now and then tears rolled down his cheeks from the corners of his reddened eyes. The men behind the front were desperately waiting to hear if the unconquerable fort had been taken.

Ali placed a white cloth over his eyes but it provided no relief, and to make matters worse, he was also suffering from an intense headache. He stood up, grasped one of the tent poles and took a few steps. He wished he could have gone to the war front and taken the unconquerable fort! For three days the Prophet's companions had been trying to take the fort but they had been unsuccessful. Every time they attacked they had been repelled suffering several deaths and grave injuries. He returned to his tent and placed his head against the main tent pole and thought about the Prophet's future. As troops passed by his tent, he noticed that some of them were injured, others walked with their heads held down, dejected, and yet others were carrying the bodies of their beloved comrades slain in battle. Ali said to himself, "If we cannot defeat these Jews of Khaibar they will unite with the *munafiqeen* (the hypocrites) and the *kuffar* (the infidels) to attack Islam and if that happens Medina will never see peace!"

Ali removed the cloth that he had placed over his swollen eyes which were burning like fire, and lay down hoping to get rid of the pain. Suddenly a messenger came from the Prophet, summoning him to come to his tent. Ali stood up and supported by the messenger, slowly walked towards the large white tent of his commander, the Prophet. The tent was crowded with officers and men. When the Prophet saw him, his face lit up and he welcomed him with an embrace and expressed concern for his illness. Companies of soldiers were returning one after another in despair. The air was filled with the cries of pain from the wounded adding to the depressing atmosphere pervading the Muslim camp. Ali stood next to the Prophet while the soldiers in the tent looked on. They said,

"This fort is unconquerable, let's make a truce."

"We can't even get near it, how could we imagine conquering it?"

"Even birds can't fly over it!"

"Silence! Everyone silence! Let's hear what our commander the Prophet of Allah has to say!"

The Prophet looked deeply into the faces of each and every one of his companions. He saw fear in their eyes but he kept his silence. He wet his finger with the saliva from his mouth and wiped it over Ali's aching eyes then he placed his hand upon Ali's head. No sooner had he done this that Ali felt his eyes gradually becoming better and his splitting headache begin to subside. All the men in the big white tent were astonished and expectantly waited for the Prophet's word. The Prophet of Allah held his son in law's hand and said confidently,

"Tomorrow, I am going to give the banner to one in whose hands lies victory and success, this man is one who loves Allah and the Prophet of Allah, and Allah and his Prophet love him."

How could victory be possible over this unconquerable fort given the weakened spirits besetting the Muslims and the companions of the Prophet?

Every soldier and every companion hoped that he would get the banner.

The next morning, after completing the prayers, the Prophet entered the big white tent with Ali, and the men waiting for him broke out in shouts of joy.

Ali came out of the white tent and sat on the dusty ground and waited for the Prophet to emerge from the tent. He came out with a banner that he had never given to anyone before. He offered it to his son-in-law and said, "Take this flag Ali, and do not stop advancing until Allah gives you victory."

Ali raised the banner aloft and waved it several times to the cheers of the soldiers. The cries of *Allahu Akbar* were carried by a fresh breeze to the distant parts of the camp injecting a new enthusiasm into the men. Not long afterwards, the young warrior mounted a red-coated Arabian stallion and galloped at full speed towards the war front followed by a fully armed battalion anxious to take on the enemy once again. The infantry, motivated by a new spirit kept marching forward following the lead of the young commander who was thundering ahead with the fluttering banner firmly in his grasp.

The unconquerable fort of Khaibar was somewhat far from the base camp and they had to reach the fort before sunrise. The land was very hilly and difficult and huge sharp thorns covered the terrain however the soldiers were courageously moving forward and eventually came in sight of the fort.

Ali pulled the reins of his horse and the soldiers halted, the horses straining at the bit in their urge to advance. Ali ordered the horsemen to tie cloths around the mouths of their horses and strike them to control their impatience. Silently and stealthily, they advanced towards the high walls of the fort. Everyone in the fort appeared to be deep in sleep except for a few guards who were patrolling the walls which were illuminated by torches to enhance security. The fort was surrounded by a deep moat full of water. This deterred horsemen from approaching the fort. After witnessing their repeated failed attempts over the last three days, the Jews inside were certain that the Muslims would never be able to conquer their fort and penetrate their defenses.

Ali reconnoitered the area and found a section of the moat that was narrow enough for him to be able to cross. He took his horse a few meters away and charged towards it successfully leaping over to the other side. Then, one by one, his men followed him, driving their horses over the moat. Just as the last soldier was about to jump, one of the guards looked over and on seeing him sounded the alarm.

"To arms! The enemy is attacking! Move it!"

"Muhammad's forces are at the walls!"

"Where is Marhab? Where is Marhab?"

"Throw down the stones! Light your arrows!"

"Marhab! Where are you?"

"Hurry…Get up here!"

A rain of fire and stones poured down upon the army of truth, but they kept their ground and held the siege. They shot arrows at the guards and made valiant attempts to break through. The commander of the fort shouted,

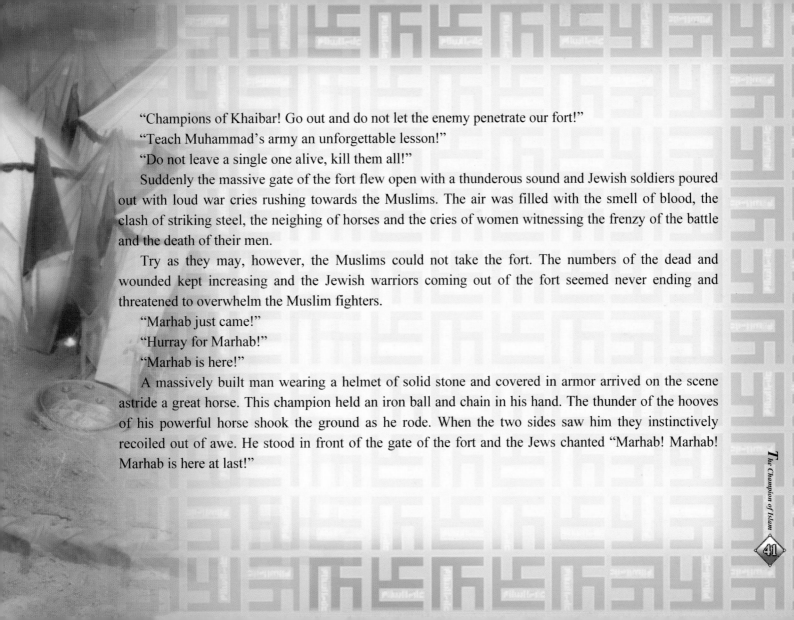

"Champions of Khaibar! Go out and do not let the enemy penetrate our fort!"

"Teach Muhammad's army an unforgettable lesson!"

"Do not leave a single one alive, kill them all!"

Suddenly the massive gate of the fort flew open with a thunderous sound and Jewish soldiers poured out with loud war cries rushing towards the Muslims. The air was filled with the smell of blood, the clash of striking steel, the neighing of horses and the cries of women witnessing the frenzy of the battle and the death of their men.

Try as they may, however, the Muslims could not take the fort. The numbers of the dead and wounded kept increasing and the Jewish warriors coming out of the fort seemed never ending and threatened to overwhelm the Muslim fighters.

"Marhab just came!"

"Hurray for Marhab!"

"Marhab is here!"

A massively built man wearing a helmet of solid stone and covered in armor arrived on the scene astride a great horse. This champion held an iron ball and chain in his hand. The thunder of the hooves of his powerful horse shook the ground as he rode. When the two sides saw him they instinctively recoiled out of awe. He stood in front of the gate of the fort and the Jews chanted "Marhab! Marhab! Marhab is here at last!"

On seeing Marhab, Ali, wearing only protective armor over his chest, rushed at the Jewish champion. The two riders circled each other, looking for an opening to attack as the two armies stood by watching. With a blood-chilling cry Marhab galloped towards Ali swinging his ball and chain. On seeing this, the Jewish women looking over the wall shrieked cries of encouragement. They were very confident that their hero would win so they derided his younger and much smaller opponent. It was a huge steel ball, almost the size of half a man's chest. It was studded with sturdy spikes of steel, and it was coming straight for Ali swinging around at incredible speed at the end of a gigantic chain. As the galloping combatants were just about to meet, our young hero deftly changed course at the last narrow minute to avoid the whirling missile. His trusty Arabian steed responded to every subtle instruction from the body of its noble rider as if they were one being. No sooner was he out of reach of the swirling ball of death, when he turned and struck his sword at the chain tangling it up hopelessly. Before Marhab could regain control, Ali gave his sword a sudden yank, wresting it from Marhab's hand and flicking it to the ground. Marhab became enraged, he had been embarrassed, and unsheathing his sword, he was now intent on killing the little upstart. Ali charged his horse towards Marhab, shouting "*Allahu Akbar*", Marhab raised his sword to counter the attack but the young hero was too fast for him, Ali struck the Jewish champion with such a powerful blow that it went straight through his shield, then through the stone helmet and continued with tremendous force through Marhab himself cleaving his skull in two down to the chin. The horse reared backwards and with a frightful scream the Jewish hero fell dead to the ground amidst the dust of the battle which enveloped the cloven body of one of the most formidable Jewish champions in Arabia.

"Run! Save yourselves! Back to the fort everyone!"

"Marhab is dead!"

"Run!"

Some of them were still fighting the Muslims and others were running back to their fort intent on closing its massive gate. On seeing this, Ali spurred his horse towards the fort. One of the Jewish fighters attacked him on his flank and in deflecting the blow, Ali lost his shield. The loss of the shield did not deter him from his goal which was to prevent the Jews from retreating into the fort and closing the gate.

The women and old men continued to throw stones and fireballs at the Muslims from atop the fort to keep the attackers away from the wall. The gate was almost closed now. Ali galloped up to the fort and grabbed the giant handle, with superhuman strength he wrenched the gate from its hinges and used it as a shield to protect himself from the lethal stones and flaming arrows raining down from above and while holding it aloft with one hand he attacked any soldier that dared to come into his path.

Afraid for their lives, the Jewish soldiers ran away, Ali tossed the gate over the moat as a bridge and the Muslim army triumphantly entered the unconquerable fort behind their young commander. That morning they saw the banner of Islam that the Prophet had given to his son-in-law fluttering over the unconquerable fort of Khaibar, conquered by the unconquerable warrior.

The Orphans' Happiest Moment

Smoke billowing out of the chimney of the old house rose into the atmosphere along with the sobbing of the children who lived there. The Imam stood in front of the house listening to them, very concerned. It sounded to him like cries of hunger. He knocked on the wooden door and eventually a middle-aged woman in tattered clothes came out. The children standing behind their mother looked weak as they stared at the stranger standing at the door. A little girl who did not seem more than five years old pointed at the pot in the yard and asked the Imam,

"Will there be any food, today?"

The mother put her hand upon her daughter's head and said, "Have patience, my dear."

"But Mama, I'm really hungry."

The Imam looked at the pot in the yard and saw that the steam that rose from it came from nothing other than boiling water.

"What do you want sir?" The woman asked.

"Where is your husband?" The Imam answered.

The lady took a deep breath and said, "My husband was a good man." She placed her hand around her son and tears welled up in her eyes as she continued to speak wistfully, "When he was alive the house was filled with love and happiness and now that he has passed away we have been ruined." Some of the children were still crying and the Imam did not ask her anything else for he realized that her heart was filled with sorrow.

He went away, rushed to his house and picked up a bag of flour, rice, some oil and a basket of dates and hurried back. It was close to noon and it was already hot so the alleys of Kufa were empty as the people stayed inside, away from the heat of the noonday sun. The mud-walls were already radiating the heat as Ali hastily made his way back to the run down house where the lonely widow and her children lived. He was perspiring profusely. On entering the alley where they lived he could still hear the cries of the orphans and their mother's entreaties to Allah. He paused at the door, wiped his brow, and knocked on the half-opened door.

After getting permission, Ali entered and immediately noticed that the mother and children were sitting in the dilapidated courtyard of the house under a half-dried palm tree crying. The fire under the cooking pot was almost out. He placed the bag of flour in the corridor and gave the oil and rice to the woman to cook and then sat with the children with a warm encouraging smile. He put his hand around the eldest and kissed his forehead and tapped the little girl on the back placing the basket of dates in front of them. When they saw the dates they were overwhelmed with joy, and stopped crying. The dates had seeds in them, so Ali sat with them and separated the seeds from the dates placing one half of a date into the girl's mouth and the other half into the boy's.

The air soon smelled of cooking rice and the mother was happily moving around the yard preparing the food while the children chatted with the Imam. He saw that the tears had left marks on their dust-covered faces so Ali sent them off to wash up. With great joy they ran to their mother speaking excitedly of the man who had brought happiness to their home. Their mother asked them to move away from the boiling pot and helped them wash their hands and faces.

"Mother, tell me when the food is ready."

"Let's go sister, let's go and play until mama calls us to eat."

They ran to Ali who asked them what they wanted to play. The little girl smiled and looked at her brother saying, "We always played horsy, horsy with our father!" To make them happy, Ali got down on all fours on the ground and started to behave like a horse walking from one side of the room to the other which made the pretty little girl extremely happy. She shrieked with delight and ran outside the room into the yard and then back again to watch her brother riding on the man who was kinder than her father. As soon as she came in, the Imam went up to her and asked her to sit on his back behind her brother. She did not need to be asked twice. She jumped for joy and immediately climbed on the Imam's back. The children laughed happily playing with the stranger and asked him to move faster which he did.

The sounds of joy and laughter filled the air and their mother, curious to see what was going on, came to see her children laughing and playing for the first time after a long while. When she saw them, she smiled with happiness for it seemed to be the happiest moment in their lives.

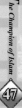

The Moon Cut to Pieces

Umm Kulthum was sitting on the stairs crying while her father was standing near the pool gazing at the star filled sky. The moon was shining behind the leaves of the date palm and seemed to be cut up into luminous pieces. She had not slept at all that night because when he had told her that he was soon to meet his Lord, she had resolved to be always at his side. Her heart was filled with sorrow. She stood up, wiped the tears from her eyes and walked towards the pool where her father was standing. As she stood next to him, once again she could not control her tears and collapsed into an uncontrollable sobbing. It was past midnight and the older the night grew the more worried she became. The ducks were also behaving strangely, they were quacking loudly and they would occasionally come up to her father and rub themselves against his feet.

He held her close to him, smiled and said,

"O my dear daughter, this night is the very night that I have been promised *shahaadah* (martyrdom)."

Umm Kulthum put her head upon her father's shoulder and he placed his hand lovingly upon her head. He took his daughter inside the house and spoke to her for a while, walking towards the window he looked at the sky once again and said,

"Yes! What the Prophet had said was the *Haqq*."

Ali left the room followed by his daughter.

"Father, please don't go, please, father please!"

The Imam came outside into the yard, made *wudu* at the pool and then walked towards the date palm. Resting his hand on the tree, he said,

"One cannot run away from what Allah has destined."

He slowly walked towards the door of the yard to leave. At that moment Umm Kulthum noticed that the ducks were running around between her father's legs trying to hold his cloak in their beaks. They flapped their wings and quacked loudly but they could not stop him from going to the door. Umm Kulthum could not control herself; she ran down the stairs towards her father and said,

"Dear father please don't go! Send Ja'da to lead the *salaat* today."

The Imam looked at his daughter's tearful face, gave her a reassuring smile and wiped away her tears with his hands and once more Umm Kulthum put her head on her father's chest and closed her eyes. When the ducks and ducklings surrounded them again the Imam said,

"Leave them alone for they will be among those who will lament for me soon."

She felt weak, and supported herself by leaning against the wall. When the Imam raised his hand to open the door, she realized that this would be the very last time she would see her father's pleasant face. Once more she collapsed into a weeping mass of tears. The Imam tried to open the door, it made a sound but it did not open. What was the problem? The Imam tried again, and again it did not open. It seemed to have become heavier than the door of Khaibar. Umm Kulthum said, "Father, the door doesn't want to open today."

The Imam placed his hands at the two ends of the door and said to himself,

"O Ali, be prepared for the last hour which is near and when death enters your house, do not cry or be sorry and do not be proud of this world no matter how much of it you might have had because soon it will change your laughter to tears of distress."

Then he lifted the door up from its hinges and placed it against the wall. When he stepped out on the street, he said,

"O my dear Lord! Make death for me a blessing and a joyous meeting!"

This was the last Umm Kulthum saw of her father, she saw him walking away from her towards the Masjid of Kufa to meet his Lord.

Hujr ibn 'Adiyy was making his night prayers in the Masjid when he realized that it had become difficult for him to breathe. He said to himself that something strange was definitely going to take place that day. He wanted to step out and refresh himself by going near the Euphrates for some time still remained before the *fajr* prayer. He stood up with some difficulty and walked towards the door of the Masjid and was surprised to hear a few people whispering in the courtyard.

"Why are you late?"

"He will be here any minute."

"O dear son, Muljim, be quick when you strike otherwise you will be the unfortunate one at dawn."

The speakers were familiar to him. It was Ash'ath the hypocrite. Everyone knew that he worked for Mu'awiyah. Hujr held his breath.

"Strike him right here."

"Do you really know Ali? No, it's better to attack him when he is in *sajdah*."

When Hujr realized that it was a conspiracy, a shiver went through his body. Who were these people? Did Mu'awiyah send them? Without delay he ran outside the Masjid without his slippers, he had to report this incident to Amir al Mu'minin before it was too late.

"Allahu Akbar, Allahu Akbar." The voice of the *mu'azzin* rang out in the cool air of dawn. Hujr ran and ran through the small narrow alleys. He paid no attention to the thorns and stones that dug into his feet. The only thing on his mind was to stop his leader from going to the Masjid but the Imam was nowhere to be seen. He finally arrived at the door of the Imam's house and heard the sound of a woman crying inside. It sounded like Umm Kulthum. He uttered a loud salaam and ran inside the house but he received no answer to his greetings. This made him more worried. The house seemed to be in utter

confusion. Hujr turned back and ran outside the house realizing that the Imam had probably taken another route so he hurried to reach the Masjid before him and tell him about the conspiracy.

"*La ilaaha illa 'Llah*"

On reaching the Masjid he saw the people standing in rows and he could hear his Imam offering the *dhikr* of the prayers. He stood up to warn the Imam but suddenly a sharp, gleaming sword appeared in the air, He shouted,

"Ya Allah…they've killed Amir al Mu'minin!"

The worshippers raised their heads from *sajdah* and ran towards the conspirator.

"Get him! It's the son of Muradi!"

"Don't let him go!"

"His name is Muljim!"

Everyone in the Masjid broke down in tears and wailing. The *mihrab* and the place of *sajdah* had turned red with the blood of the Imam. His sons took hold of him at his two sides and lifted him up carrying him away from the Masjid. The Imam, mortally wounded by a poisoned sword had turned pale. Death was inevitable. Imam Ali smiled to himself and said,

"By the Lord of the Ka'ba I have been successful."

List of Illustrations

Nine Hadith from Hazrat Ali (a.s)

- The writing of a man shows his intellect and the quality of his character.

- Egotism is a barrier to development and perfection.

- One who points out your mistakes is like one who gives you a gift.

- Grief comes from giving up opportunities.

- Learn the Qur'an and contemplate upon it for it is the best of speech and the wellspring of life.

- Seek knowledge for if you are rich it will increase your beauty and attractiveness and if you are poor it will protect you from falling down.

- Whoever seeks advice will not fall into destruction.

- The worst of friends is one who talks sweetly with you and hides your faults from you.

- Correcting someone in front of others is like destroying his character.

Sources

1. *Kashf al Ghummah*
2. *Irshaad of Sheikh Mufid*
3. *Bihaar al Anwaar Vol.1*
4. *Tarikh al Tabary*
5. *Hayaat al Qulub*
6. *Tarikh-e-Payambar*
7. *Majaalis al Muttaqeen*
8. *Shajarah al Tuba*
9. *Muntaha al Amal*